S0-BYX-550

Bizzie the Beat-Loving Bumbling Bee
Text copyright © 2020 Janet Lawless Christ
Illustrations copyright © 2020 Janet Lawless Christ

Illustrations and design by Ryan Hernandez.
The illustrations for this book were executed in Photoshop.
The text type is Goldenbook.

All rights reserved.

For information about permission to reproduce selections from this book,
write to JoyWorks Networks, Inc.,
P.O. Box 7136, Rancho Santa Fe, CA 92067.

Printed in the United States of America.

ISBN 978-1-7354478-3-4

Print Broker SGS Enterprises

www.JoyWorksNetworks.com

Like us on Facebook
Follow us on Twitter and Instagram
Contact us for Special Volume Discounts

BIZZIE

THE BEAT-LOVING BUMBLING BEE

To all the artists and musicians who have mesmerized me from
mega venues to my own backyard…

Bucky Pizzarelli	Joel Gomez
John Pizzarelli	Mel Torme
Harry Savino	Israel Moldando
Archie Ruchstuhl	Nathan Rivera
Ed Lawless	Russell Cassalione
Bill Collins	The Fred Benedetti Trio
Peter Allen	Dawn Mitschele
Diana Krall	Gayle Skidmore
Billy Dean	George Winston
Austin Burns	Trevor Davis
Paul Williams	Bobby Caldwell
Al Jareau	Chris Botti
Natalie Cole	Steve Tyrell
David Benoit	Boz Scaggs
Harry Connick Jr.	Susan Egan
Michael Bublé	Rosemary Clooney
Rod Stewart	Susan Muha
Sonia Miro	

…and Kenny Loggins, who reminded me when I needed it the most,
"Love should teach you joy."

A portion of the proceeds will go to 501(c)3 Guitars for the Classroom.

Not long ago, in a place near and dear to your heart, was the Land of Second Chances.
And in that lovely land there was a silly village named "JoyWorks Junction."
In that silly village there lived a busy, buzzing bee named "Bizzie" (...of course!).

Bizzie and her buddies just loved life buzzing around the plants and flowers of The Inn at JoyWorks Junction. Bizzie especially loved the beat of the music that played throughout The Inn each day.

Bizzie, the leader of her buzzing bee pack, took her job very seriously indeed.

She and her buddies buzzed about toting pollen on their knees and spreading it to the plan
and flowers so The Inn's guests wouldn't sneeze from the pollen-filled breeze.

But because the musical beats brought her joy, sometimes, despite her best intentions, Bizzie bumbled into trouble bringing her bee buds with her.

Some evenings at dusk when she heard the sounds of smooth jazz, Bizzie let her buddies bumble and they (oops!) bumped into the giggling guests on the Terrace.

Some afternoons, classical interludes enchanted her and they (uh oh!) inadvertently startled the snoozing sunbathers at the pool.

And some mornings, purely by accident, soothing meditative lute tunes allured her, and her buds (whoops!) peeved the posing yogis in the spa.

The Inn's very kind and compassionate Human Manager Michelle never wanted to bother Bizzie and her buddies. But Bizzie and her beat-loving bumbling were troubling, so Human Michelle needed to find them a new place to buzz to their hearts' content.

An idea buzzed into her brain! It was to re-home Bizzie and her
buddies to a safer, happier place, like The Fanciful Bee Farm just down
the road in east JoyWorks Junction. But "how?" was the question.

Until she could figure out how to do just that without harming any living creature, she came up with a nifty idea to distract Bizzie and her buzzing buddies.

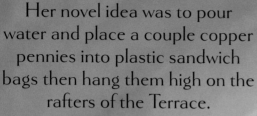

Her novel idea was to pour water and place a couple copper pennies into plastic sandwich bags then hang them high on the rafters of the Terrace.

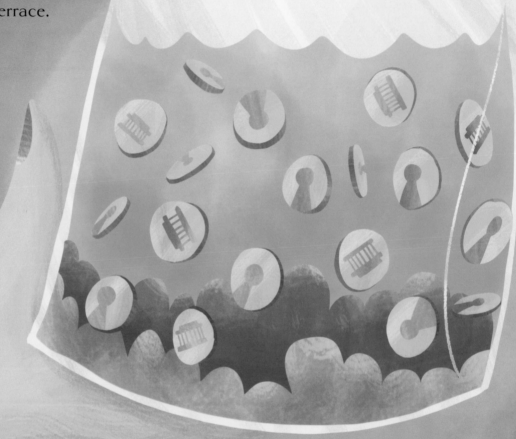

You see the bees mistake the shimmering bags for hornet nests so they steer clear! Busy bees certainly don't want to spar with ornery hornets.

Just as Human Michelle was placing the last of the tricky shimmering bags high on a rafter, something strange and wondrous occurred...

Lilting through the late afternoon air, she heard the sweet sounds of strumming. And peeking around the corner, she spied a musical artist magically musing while he played his ukulele.

Who else was drawn to the beautiful beat of the mysterious musical artist's ukulele?

Because Bizzie so loved the sounds of music - jazz, classical, meditative, and now (best of all) ukulele - she joyfully brought her buddies to have a listen and buzz high above the mysterious musician.

They popped to the plucking and did not bother him.

They swooped to the strums and did not bother him.

They jived to the jams and did not bother him.

Seeing Bizzie and her buddies buzzing high above yet seeming not to bumble and trouble the musician, another nifty notion popped into Human Michelle's very, very, very clever and loving noggin.

She politely waited until the musing musician was done playing his joyful tune. "Welcome to The Inn at JoyWorks Junction," said Human Michelle as she held out her hand for a hearty handshake. But the musician merely smiled kind-of-but-not-altogether toward Human Michelle and replied, "Hello there, I'm Joel."

"I noticed that the bee buddies were hovering overhead just loving the humming sounds of your ukulele," said Human Michelle. "Are they perchance bothering you?"

"Oh, are busy bees buzzing above?" Human Musician Joel smiled and said. "I couldn't hear them above the sounds of my songs and I cannot see them because I am legally blind." 21

Human Michelle was baffled by the discovery that Human Musician Joel
was blind to both the sight and to the bother of the bees.

Human Joel continued, "Kind creatures of all kinds are drawn to the calming sounds of music.
And in the joyful world of calming sounds, the ukulele hums like no other. Since I cannot see the bees
and they really mean me no harm, we just get along and enjoy the song."

Even more bewildered, but certainly delighted, Human Michelle hatched her
very, very, very clever plan which she whispered to Human Joel.

At the stroke of dusk, as the sun was dipping into the horizon, just in time to be tucked in for the night, Human Michelle and Human Joel hopped aboard The Inn's JoyWorks Junction Jitney!

There in the back seat, Human Joel began strumming the sweet sounds of his ukulele.

As they tootled off in the direction of The Fanciful Bee Farm, the most bewitching (or is it "bee-witching?") sight could be seen - by those who can see, of course.

izzie wasn't bumbling but parading with a purpose. You see, she knew now was the right time to follow the music. She was leading her bee buddies away from The Inn to their new fanciful bee-friendly home. Following Human Joel's music, they were being "re-homed" to a place where they could joyfully buzz, pop, swoop, and jive, and never bother a being.

You see, we all should be mindful (or is it "bee" mindful?) of the fact that in life, sometimes when it might feel like it's bad and sad and scary to have to move away, it's really okay to be re-homed. Joy works when...you follow sweet sounds that make your heart sing. And Zooper Heroes love the oh-so-sweet sounds of calm and safe second chances.

28

Psst...That was the evening when Human Michelle and Human Joel became Human Zooper Heroes too, because they gave fellow creatures a second chance. Little did they know what they would find when they tootled back to The Inn at JoyWorks Junction!

(Stay tuned for more jolly joy...and for a sneak peek at exactly what and who just might be a Zooper Hero!)

GLOSSARY

BAFFLE - To confuse or puzzle

BEWITCHING/ENCHANTED - Charming and delightful

CLEVER - Quick in thinking and learning

COMPASSIONATE - Being able to understand others and wanting to help them

INADVERTENT/UNINTENTIONAL - Not on purpose

INTERLUDE - Anything that fills the space between two happenings

LILT - A light, swaying song

NIFTY - Good and smart

NOGGIN - A person's head

PERCHANCE - Maybe

RE-HOME - To find a new place to live

SHIMMER - To shine with an unsteady light

UKULELE - A small guitar with four strings

Writer

Janet Lawless Christ loves life with her husband and her ever-growing menagerie a-plenty in Rancho Santa Fe, CA. She is "Human Mama" to a growing brood of kiddos and grandkids, too. After a robust real estate and business career, Janet founded JoyWorks Networks, Inc. and also turned her attention to crafting a series of children's stories about finding and holding on to nuggets of joy. Her goal is to generate awareness and funds for oh-so-deserving non-profit organizations.

Other works by Janet Lawless Christ

Nugget the Nomad ...Adventures of a Yoga Dog
Published Sept. 2020, 2nd Edition published Nov. 2020
Nugget El Nomad
Spanish Edition published Nov. 2020

Coming sooner than soon…
Quinn at The Inn
'Twas Joy Jubilance Day
Hogan the Hero
Bertha the Earthworm and Her Chance Encounter
Niblick the Theater Chick
Cooper and His Cancer Answer
Barry the Berry Hungry Baby Bear

...and more adorable adventures from the critters in JoyWorks Junction.

Illustrator and Designer

Ryan Hernandez was born and raised in Southern California and graduated from CSUF with a degree in Fine Arts Illustration. He currently lives in Valencia, CA, with his wife, two children, and labrador, Fred. He has created illustrations for various art shows around Los Angeles and freelances all over the city for studios such as Nickelodeon, Disney, Titmouse, Netflix, and DreamWorks.